pitman 2000 SHORTHAND

First Course Facility Drills
Second Edition

Bryan Coombs

Pitman

PITMAN BOOKS LIMITED
128 Long Acre, London WC2E 9AN

Associated Companies
Pitman Publishing Pty Ltd, Melbourne
Pitman Publishing New Zealand Ltd, Wellington

© Pitman Books Limited, 1982

First edition 1975
Second edition 1982
Reprinted 1982

Isaac Pitman

Text set in 10/11 pt Linotron 202 Bembo
Printed and bound in Great Britain at The Pitman Press, Bath

ISBN 0 273 01806 X
H2 2042:26

700 Common-word Reading and Dictation Exercises

This text comprises 42 shorthand reading passages which use the 700 common outlines and their derivatives. A longhand key, counted in tens, is provided at the back of the book which includes alphabetical lists of the 700 common outlines and their derivatives.

ISBN 273 01255 X

The Life of Sir Isaac Pitman
(Inventor of Phonography)

Reissue Centenary Edition

Alfred Baker

A near facsimile reissue of the 1913 Centenary Edition detailing the life and work of Sir Isaac Pitman. For those who know and use Pitman's Shorthand, this book offers a fascinating background — how the basic shorthand characters were devised and how the first Penny Plate taught the complete shorthand system on one sheet of paper. It contains a wealth of personal detail about Sir Isaac's rich and varied experience as an exponent of the 'Reading, Writing and Reckoning Reform'.

- Introduction by Sir James Pitman, KBE, grandson of Sir Isaac Pitman
- Social document on life in Victorian England
- Reprint of Stenographic Sound-Hand published in 1837

216 × 138 mm/448 pages/
Cased ISBN 0 273 01587 7

Pitman's Shorthand Speed Examination Practice No. 1

This book contains a selection of the shorthand examination material set by the RSA, the LCCI and ScotBEC during 1978. The material is written in Pitman 2000 Shorthand with a longhand key at the back of the book counted in tens for dictation.

- Speed range from 50 wpm to 120 wpm.

216 × 138 mm/128 pages/Paper
ISBN 0 273 01500 1

Pitman 2000 Shorthand Pocket Dictionary

A pocket-sized guide to the shorthand outlines for approximately 20,000 of the more common words in the English language. The outlines show position writing and are written in fully vocalized shorthand. All the short forms and most of the derivatives are shown italicized.

ISBN 273 01810 8

Pitman 2000 Shorthand First Course Review

Bryan Coombs

A complete revision of Pitman 2000 Shorthand theory with a further extension of the vocabulary. Each chapter contains a theory introduction, a short form drill and a correspondence section, with longhand counted in tens for dictation. Throughout, the text is designed to aid rapid reading and writing. Five cassettes contain all the practice material from First Course Review — dictated first at 70 wpm and then at 90 wpm.

ISBN 273 01801 9

PREFACE

First Course Facility Drills (second edition), are related to the working vocabulary and theory in each unit of *Pitman 2000 Shorthand First Course* (second edition).

When using this drill book a pen is, unquestionably, the best writing implement because the 'thin' or 'thick' strokes produced by other writing implements are much less accurate and therefore more difficult to transcribe. The nib of the pen needs to be flexible so that it responds immediately to the slightest changes in pressure; it needs to be fluent so that it will move swiftly and smoothly over the paper, giving an even, continuous line.

The 'thin' or 'thick' strokes which are necessary for accurate transcription are only consistently possible when written with a carefully chosen shorthand pen. Ideally, one should try out several nibs until the necessary flexibility and fluency of line is attained because individual needs differ.

The cap should be removed from the pen and the pen should be held lightly between the index and second fingers of the writing hand with the thumb lying along the other side of the 'triangle' to give control. It should not be gripped tightly with tense fingers, but with only sufficient force for it to remain in the hand without sliding out. The fingers should be no more than slightly curved with the little finger only in contact with the writing surface. These may seem small, even insignificant, details but their importance in establishing good writing habits is very great.

Page turning occurs frequently during each session of drilling or dictation. It must be completed with ease and speed. Keep the page on which you are writing flat, but take hold of the bottom corner of that page with the finger and thumb of the non-writing hand so that as the last line of shorthand is completed you can quickly flick the page over.

Work through *First Course Facility Drills* in the following way:
read each line of printed shorthand;
study the outlines;
copy the outlines carefully on the first blank line, writing across the page.

Compare your shorthand with the printed outlines, and then write again on the second blank line as quickly and accurately as possible from dictation, or saying the words to yourself as you write.

The Pitman 2000 Dictionary of English and Shorthand

Containing the shorthand outlines and meanings of over 75000 words, this invaluable work of reference includes a summary of the changes in the Pitman 2000 form of Pitman's Shorthand. American pronunciation and spelling is included with cross-referenced entries showing the differences.

216 × 138 mm/848 pages/Cased
ISBN 0 273 01618 0

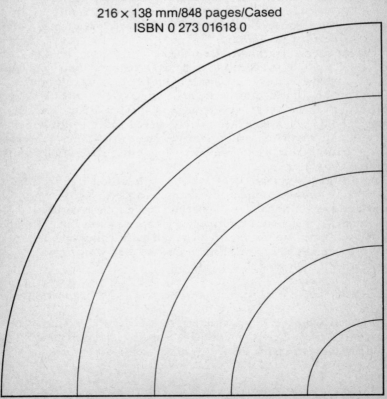

UNIT 1 *Drill 1*

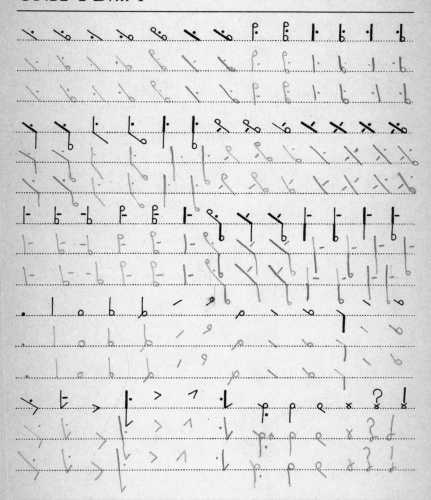

UNIT 1 *Drill 2*

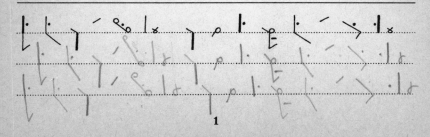

UNIT 25 *Drill 50*

Notwithstanding the uncomfortable weather, please disconnect all of the 200 air-conditioning units and the conveyor belt.

From the considerable profit of £1,500,000 a high dividend will be recommended for all the shareholders.

With 500 shares he continues to have complete control and confirms all appointments and computer contracts.

In recognition of his services the company made a considerable contribution to the comprehensive retirement fund.

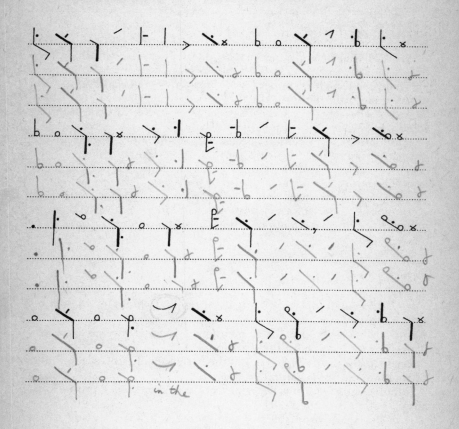

in the

UNIT 2 *Drill 3*

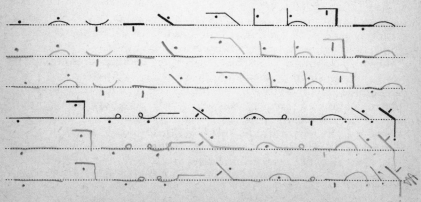

UNIT 24 *Drill 47*

nation, national, attention, divisions, relations, fashions, fashionable, profession, professional, sessions, solution.

mention, mentioned, co-operation, direction, option, addition, additional, collection, international.

election, selection, location, affectionate, vocation, action, caution, station, stationery, exceptional.

position, positions, decision, decisions, organization, organizations, physician, association, transition, proposition, sensational.

television, pensionable, mentionable, unnecessary, illegal, unhappy, non-delivery.

satisfaction, information, large corporation, this corporation, these corporations, unsatisfactory, immediate attention, prompt attention, your attention, give attention, whole attention, my attention.

UNIT 24 *Drill 48*

Your attention is drawn to the selection of fashions in the spring collections in Paris.

Additional taxation has been mentioned as one way to clear the national debt and relieve the situation.

Special attention should be paid to the exceptionally fine organization of such a remarkably large corporation.

Additional information is necessary and you should seek professional advice before making a decision.

The position is pensionable but you should watch for omissions and seek a decision from the lawyer.

UNIT 25 *Drill 49*

conditions, controls, continue, continuous, considerable, connects, connection, confirm, concern, conference, commit.

common, commonly, company, complete, completed, completion, comment, constant, convenient, convenience, computer.

discontinue, incomplete, uncommon, recommended, recommendation, reconsider, disconnect, uncomfortable, recognize, recognition.

circumstance, circumstances, self-control, self-contained, subconscious, inconsistent, attitude, substitute, institute, destitute.

We are confident, I am confident, we shall continue, I will consider, they will consider, this committee, very common, nevertheless, notwithstanding.

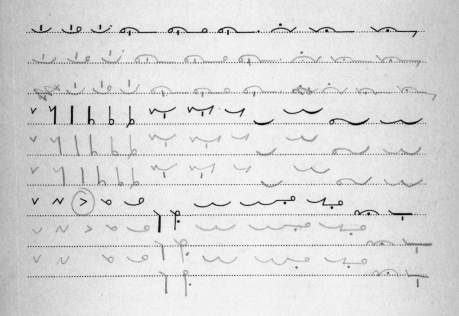

UNIT 2 *Drill 4*

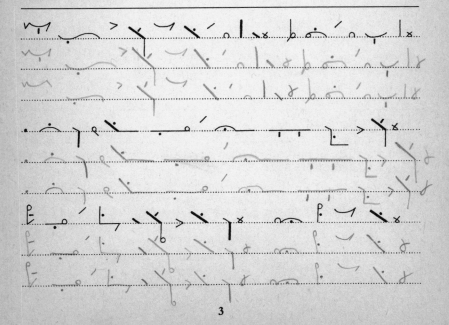

instead of the, you have, you have been, who have, which have, better off.

1, 2, 3, 4, 5, 6, 7, 8, 9, 10, 100, 3,000 tonnes, £7,000.

UNIT 22 *Drill 44*

You have been advanced £5000 but you have not made any profits for the firm this year.

It has proved to be a difficult market for profits according to our representatives in the provinces.

Although we have had many difficulties, the weather has improved and the harvest should be good.

This provides positive proof of his achievements over a number of years as chief executive.

Part of our reserves—say £20,000—can be used for photographic supplies.

UNIT 23 *Drill 45*

centre, centred, order, ordered, picture, pictured, wonder, wondered. materials, after, afternoon, future, letter/leather, chapter, distributors, directors.

wonderful/wonderfully, January, therefore, interview, my order, their order, under, later.

my letter, your letter, their letter, in your letter, I have been, I have been there, I know, I know there is.

I think there is, if there is, I can be, I can be there, I will be, I will be there, later than the, some other way, for there/their.

UNIT 23 *Drill 46*

We know there is a wonderful future in this country, and therefore you should accept the offer.

Make out your order immediately for further supplies and ask for delivery in January.

Typewritten letters present a picture of your firm to the reader and should be orderly.

I have been there in the afternoon and it was busy, but I will try a morning visit soon.

The January sales are an example of ordered chaos, but I will be there to buy a coat.

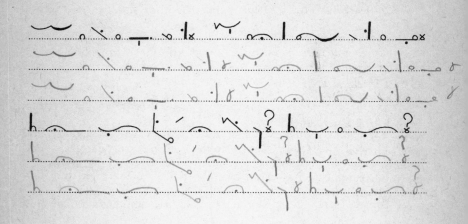

UNIT 3 *Drill 5*

4

It is safer to refer to the reference books, and I do so frequently when in doubt.

There is a rumour that altogether it has not been a very satisfactory arrangement but there is nothing we can do other than accept it.

We have been to the Thursday meetings before and I gather they are now very much better than they were last year.

UNIT 21 *Drill 41*

flow, flowed, fly, flies, floor, flowers, flurry, travels, travelled, helpful, helpfully, beautiful.

doubtful, delightful, powerful, careful, final, finalize, original, essential, special, official, initial.

rival, novel, level, fulfil, film, canal, manual, influential, thankful, enlarge.

as early as possible, it is possible, it is not possible, as soon as possible, as soon as we can, this month, next month, several months, United States, United States of America.

UNIT 21 *Drill 42*

Flying today is dull and rival firms offer films and drinks to the travellers.

We are taking a special tour to your country as soon as possible to see the rivers and beautiful flowers.

Next month an official from our company in the United States is flying over to finalize the budget.

There is no available space but it will be several months before approval is given to enlarge this factory.

Use this special polish and the beautiful wood floor will develop a fine wax shine.

UNIT 22 *Drill 43*

above, behalf, forgive, representative, served, deserved, proved, reserved, halved, achieved, observed.

serves, deserves, proves/proofs, gives, relatives, halves, achieves, observes, drives, gift, draft, rift, drift.

advance, advantage, profit, definitely, defend, defence, provide, traffic, provinces, graphic, activity.

cough, coffee, heave, heavy, move, knife, roughly, chiefly, briefly, approval, positively.

difficult, difficulty, part of, number of, member of, in spite of the,

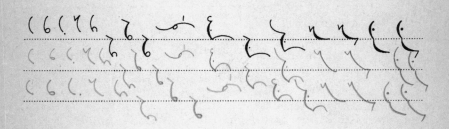

UNIT 3 *Drill 6*

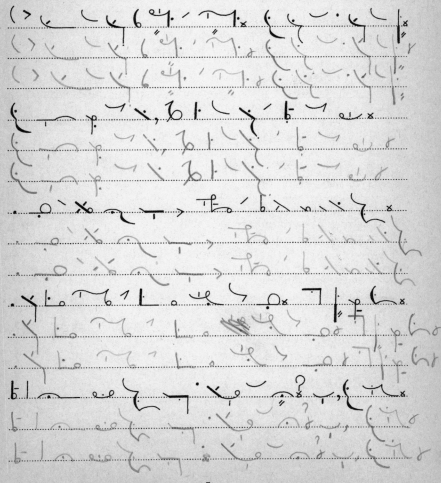

5

UNIT 19 *Drill 37*

quickly, qualify, quantity, subsequent, question, equal, quite, quality, query.

requires, quietly, inquire, inquiry, liquid, adequate, square, language. where, while, when, white, wheel, why, meanwhile, elsewhere, knowledge, acknowledge.

we will inquire, we have enquired, they have enquired, several inquiries, your inquiry, our inquiry, we shall require, you may require, will be required, office requirements, your requirements.

UNIT 19 *Drill 38*

We shall require someone who is well qualified in languages and shorthand for this post.

Please acknowledge all the recent enquiries about the language posts and direct subsequent queries to me.

Where can a person qualify, and what are the total costs involved?

We have had requests for the new white correcting liquid which you manufacture for office requirements.

Your knowledge of the equipment is equal to none and you will be required to take charge when it is installed.

UNIT 20 *Drill 39*

free, fruit, Friday, frighten, throw, through/threw, freeze/frees, shrug, shred, fresh, frame, freight.

offers, either, pressure, measured, measurement, average, differ, difference, over, otherwise, favourable, advertise.

forget, foresee, sever, summer, sooner, murmur, river, discover, gather, however, rather.

together, altogether, satisfactory, very, very satisfactory, very much, very little, there, there is, there are, there will be.

there is no, I gather, more, more than, more time, sooner than, before, from, from us, from every, commercial.

UNIT 20 *Drill 40*

We have been offered more than expected for the commercial property near the river.

You will discover there is very little difference in the policy on energy between the two parties.

UNIT 4 *Drill* 7

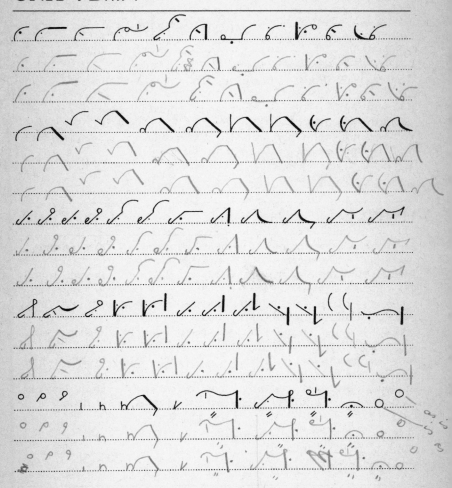

UNIT 4 *Drill* 8

UNIT 17 *Drill 34*

We cannot be responsible for your belongings and they are left entirely at your own risk.

I did not know how long the train would take on the eastern to western run across the plains.

We have been almost ruined in the economic decline but the accountant is optimistic.

You will find that a better effect can be gained by drawing a fine line round the painting.

You will not be disappointed with the results if you spend an hour working on your own each evening this week.

UNIT 18 *Drill 35*

department, experiment, apartment, adjustment, pronouncement, assortment, announcement, appointment, attainment.

amendment, disappointment, only, unless, until, annual, nylon, unlock, unload, canal, inlay.

analyse, analysis, unlicensed, endless, wrongly, strongly, experimental, departmental, monumental.

boldly, deeply, cheaply, daily, hardly, lovely, lively, keenly, apparently.

actually, eventually, solely, wholly, singly, physically, locally, legally, totally, vitally.

suddenly, urgently, certainly, mainly, patiently, plainly, evenly, particularly, accordingly, sales department, your department.

UNIT 18 *Drill 36*

An announcement about a new appointment in the Sales Department is expected on Monday.

Apparently help is urgently needed and we are certainly prepared to assist for a time.

Annual results in your Department are a disappointment and an analysis is necessary to find the reason.

The experiment was successful and amendments will be made to our appointments system accordingly.

A postponement now will cause resentment but it is hardly likely to happen at this stage.

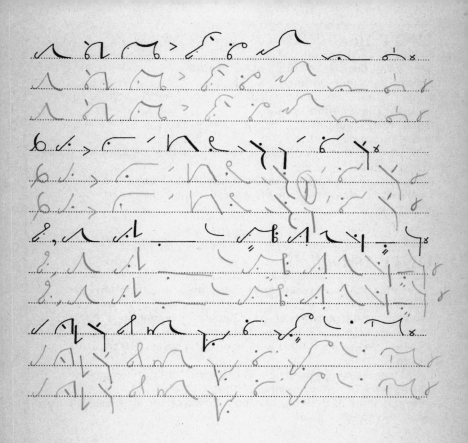

UNIT 5 *Drill 9*

7

UNIT 16 *Drill 31*

line, loan, then, than, thin, man, vein/vain, woman, mean, mine, opinion, genuine, within.

union, earns, machines, telephones, examines, outlines, assigns, means, balloons, fines, refines.

fence, fences, announces, balances, allowances, occurrences, insurances, mind, demand.

mint, event, find, demand, payment, efficient, sufficient, funny, many, avenue, revenue.

illness, manpower, businessman, you will not, I am not, it will not be, I will not be, this arrangement, we will arrange, I have arranged, I am arranging.

UNIT 16 *Drill 32*

Men and women operate many machines in offices and factories today.

I am arranging a meeting on Thursday evening to announce the settlement and in my opinion it is genuine.

The fine old avenue is lined with trees and it will not be the same if it is fenced.

As a businessman I know this arrangement will produce new revenue and increase our investments.

I am not alone in thinking that this allowance for insurance is far too small and should be augmented.

UNIT 17 *Drill 33*

pain/pane, town, June, can, gain, grown, green, brown, train, brain, drawn, between.

win, wine, eastern, western, ruin, modern, turn, return, burn, adjourn, learn.

happen, maintain, written, suggestion, garden, certain, London, fortune, curtain, kitchen.

begins, engines, once, joins, runs, declines, expenses, against, assistance, attendance, ripens, bones.

student, hand, ground, wants, spends, correspond, important, rained, rainy, deny, bonus.

handwritten, landlord, cannot, responsible, gentleman, gentlemen, I cannot, you will not, do not, have been, better than, our own, we are not.

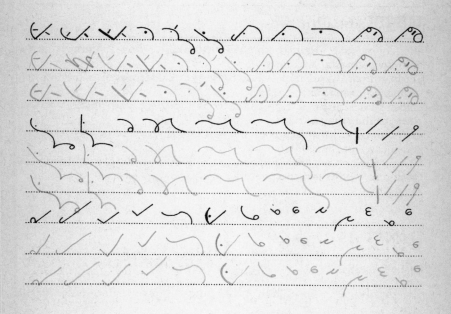

UNIT 5 *Drill 10*

8

UNIT 14 *Drill 28*

It is your duty to take this opportunity to discuss your security problems with the experts.

Will you allow our new design manager to visit you to discuss the issues you raised?

Now you will be able to make your regular trip to New York to inspect the antiques.

In your view, how secure are the new newspaper and beauty products businesses in the capital?

About how much are you paying each individual to plough the fields to the south of the creek?

UNIT 15 *Drill 29*

usual, garage, visual, he, hope, happiness, high, highest, head, hatch, hike.

height, hotel, whose, hot, heat, hurry, house, habit, hard, hark, harvest.

perhaps, prohibit, adhere, household, leasehold, mishap, racehorse, home, him, her, holiday.

hold, hire, hill, whole/hole, helper, harm, humble, hear/here, heard, hurt, heart, heartless, hearty.

he is, he will, he will be, he was, if he, if he is/has, if he will, if he will be, if he was, I think he will, I know that he is/has.

I know that he will, I hope, we hope, I hope you will, we hope you will, I hope you will be able to, we hope that you will be able to, I hope that he.

UNIT 15 *Drill 30*

I think he will take his holidays at the usual time of the year and stay in the same hotel near the harbour.

We have just heard that you are back and we hope you will be able to visit the new houses soon.

Perhaps the mortgage on a new house will be too high right now and we should stay here.

I know that he is going to hire a car for the whole holiday but he will have to hurry.

The headmaster had a mishap with the car and hurt himself but he is better now.

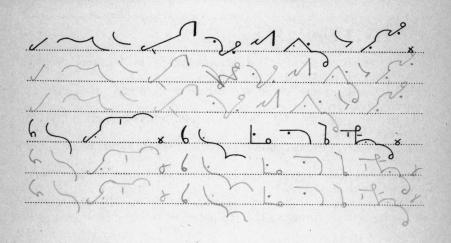

UNIT 6 *Drill 11*

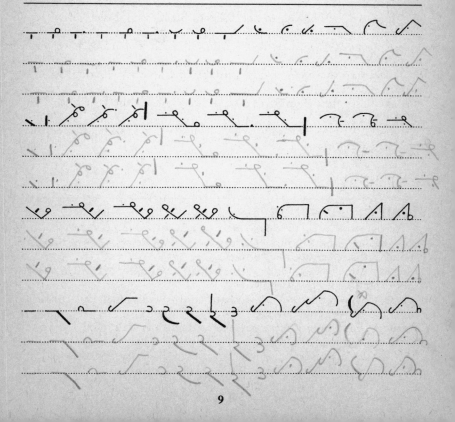

9

UNIT 13 *Drill 25*

eat, she, each, please, ease, seen/scene, reach, teach, deep, deeper, zero, succeed, read/reed, legal.

dealing, deed, leaving, cheapest, clearing, week/weak, meals, people, believe, treat, treason.

ill, sit, bill, brings, did, listed, simple, figures, limit, rhythm, statistics, industry.

wish, increase, business, build, blue, true, school, tour, book, look, goods.

mistake, discuss, receive, money, sister, system, easy, lazy, idea, radio, area, audio.

Mrs, puts, putting, to be, to be able to, year, in this city, if you will, let us have, your business, at least, please let us know, our business.

UNIT 13 *Drill 26*

We think we shall be able to build up our business in this city next year and have a share of the market.

Please visit Mrs Smith who has cracked a rib and let us have your report this week.

At least admit that many of the mistakes this year are in your area and should be put right.

I think these latest figures reveal a limited loss for the year to the end of July.

We think it is clear that any large business is going to be pleased that the rates are not going up.

UNIT 14 *Drill 27*

out, mouth, loud, lounge, crowded, announcing, doubt, about, spout, refuses, new/knew, power.

Tuesday, few, issued, feud, value, valuable, volume, occupy, assume, shout, south, plough, doubts.

secure, duty, opportunity, fortunate, issues, individual, due, queues/cues, rescue, revenue, argue.

situated, graduate, fewer, reviewer, duet, mutual, dual, regulate, circulate, fixture.

how, how much, subject, subjects, subjected, subjecting, this subject, these subjects, in this subject, New York, are you.

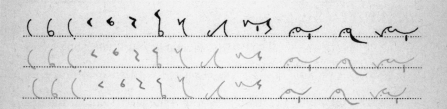

UNIT 6 *Drill 12*

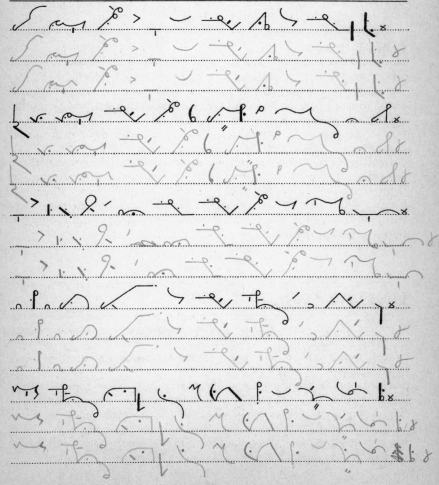

10

UNIT 11 *Drill 22*

All the tests suggest that the chest is affected by smoking, so it would be wise to stop immediately.

The Master of the four-masted vessel set sail with gusto and in great style.

They were all standing in mud by the end of the match and for the first time the guests lost the game.

We buy the latest styles just as fast as they are manufactured and suggest that you talk to our staff.

Write immediately or just as fast as you are able and stop them wasting cash on posters.

UNIT 12 *Drill 23*

try, trust, trap, dry, address, drop, price, present, bright, brought, across, grow, protest, transfer.

problem, number, prepare, locker, trader, labour, strayed, straight, strike, soccer, surprise.

makers, remembers, correct, programme, express, destroy, records, recording.

dear, larger, according/according to, particular, particulars, trade/toward, trades/towards, trading, dear sir, dear madam, at present, for the present.

I regret, we regret, yours faithfully, yours sincerely, this company, your company, for the company, our company, Paper Company Limited, oil company.

UNIT 12 *Drill 24*

I remember you and I trust that your company is making some progress this autumn.

I must stress we have had the problem of no water for months in this paper company.

Subscribe today and the price will be better for you and your members in the trade.

According to the records of this company the numbers at the trade fair were larger in October.

We regret having to charge extra for all the paper products but prices are rising fast.

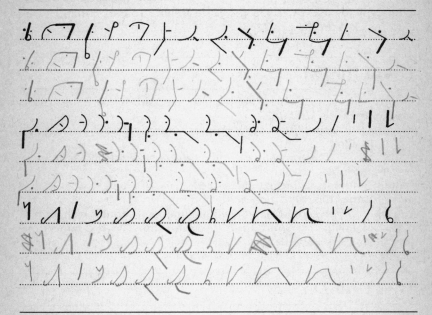

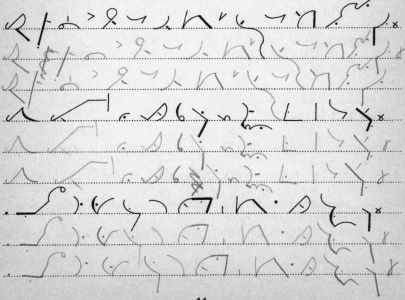

Who is largely to blame for all those glaring errors and the muddle with the sample labels?

Who will be able to tackle the large double role of smuggler and customs clerk in the play?

UNIT 10 *Drill 19*

by/buy, time, wide, nice, apply, like, file, site/sight, light, arrive, supply, exercise, exhaust.

item, isolate, deny, boy, enjoy, employ, night, voice, choice, rejoice, coy, toil, alloy.

avoid, avoids, unavoidable, oil, oils, buyers, via, science, employee, royal, enjoyable, voyage.

should, without, influence, influenced, several, I will, I was, I am, I may, I came, I expect.

you should, you should be, you should not be, it should, it should be, it should not be, at some time, for some time, at the same time, several times, several days.

UNIT 10 *Drill 20*

Short form exercises should be enjoyed and to develop the right pace they should be timed as you do them.

A nice fire is a rare sight today and a delight at this cold time.

I will be exhausted by the time I arrive but I have no choice of bus that night.

Employers and employees have a choice in a range of jobs in textiles. Both the daylight and night fighting have stopped and the oil is supplied via the pipe as desired.

UNIT 11 *Drill 21*

stock, stop, next, most, lost, last, store, staircase, start, starting, style, just, stem.

tests, suggests, guests, posts, lasts, rests, bursts, coasts, wastes, boasts, beset, gusto, upset.

master, masters, mastered, jester, Chester, faster, foster, cluster, clusters, poster, posters, duster, dusters.

mud, made, mad, madam, end, ends, ending, send, sends, sending, stand, stands, standing, descend, descending, standard.

immediate, immediately, largest, almost, first, at first, first time, for the first time, first class, as fast as, just as.

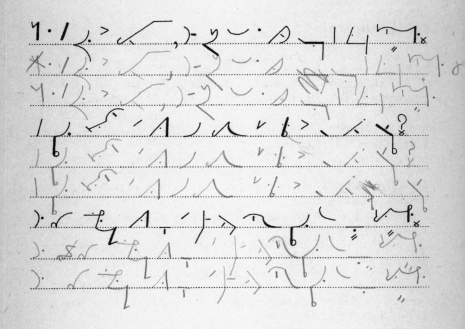

UNIT 8 *Drill 15*

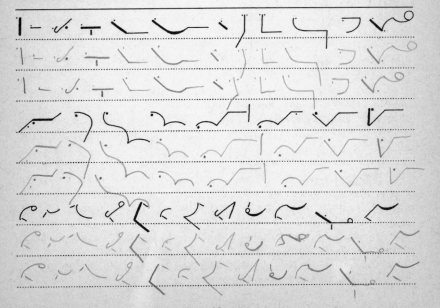

12

UNIT 8 *Drill 15*

add, act, away, ago, back, bank, bad, attach, attack, fact, cash, balances.
regard, arch, farm, arm, marked, market, park, dark.
loss, not, off, was, job, lot, shop, watch, song, long, because, wrong.
law, talk, cause, small, tall, saw, caught, thought, bought, lawyer, walk, raw, sauce/saws.
ought, always, although, also, small charge, our charges, top form, bank form, tomorrow, owe, owes, owing, owed, was not.

UNIT 8 *Drill 16*

A small charge will be added for doing the job on the shop on a Saturday or Sunday.
The watch I bought was always wrong and the charges for repairs were not small.
A song which is top in the pop charts makes lots of cash and swells some pockets.
Our lawyer thinks we ought to take this form back to the bank and ask for cash.
We shall pay off the sum we owe because it is not a lot and it makes sense to do so.

UNIT 9 *Drill 17*

play, plate, apple, pleasant, pledge, blow, blows, blame, black, able, rubble, enable, unable.
total, totals, bottle, meddle/medal, muddle, enclose, enclosed, claim, class, glass, clothes.
plays/place, placing, placings, settles, settling, settled, explores, capable, table, sample, exclaim, shuttle.
who, who will, who will be, who are, who is/who has, largely, able to, able to make, able to think, we are able to, unable to, you will be able to.

UNIT 9 *Drill 18*

Your Uncle Tom was unable to settle the muddled claim and the case is closed.
The total claimed is enclosed and the debt may be settled at your local bank.
Those who worked on Sunday claimed double rates and we shall have to settle today or tomorrow.

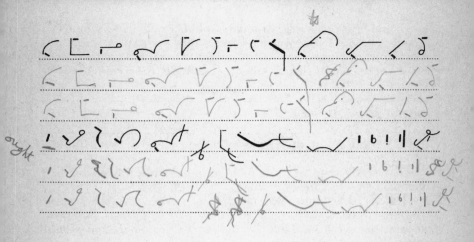

UNIT 8 *Drill 16*

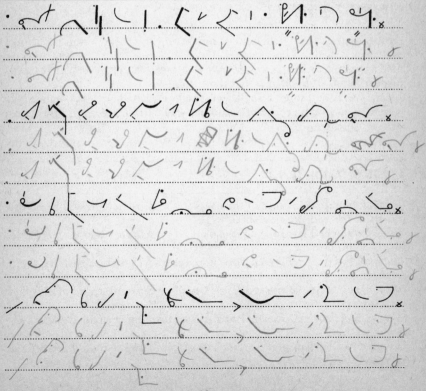

13

could, could be, you could, we could, would, would have, would be, it would be, would you, were, we were, they were, were you.
think, thinks, thinking, that, that is, all that, that it is, I think, we think, I know that the, let us know, let us have, to let you know.

UNIT 6 *Drill 12*

We will let you know the results of the cut in export rates for the expected debate.
It would be too late to let us know the export results this Wednesday as the manufacturers met yesterday.
Cut all the dead bedding roses and you may expect expert results in the months to come.
You said you were working for the export customers and would report today.
I know that the customers located the fair and I think they will be staying in Rome for some days.

UNIT 7 *Drill 13*

ages, luggage, jets, such, much, touch, show, shape, budget, change, exchange, check/cheque, page, shut.
shade, rush, us, say, sowed/sewed, estate, escape, escaped, essays, suspect, shall, which, on, had, had the.
I had, we had, large, I shall, we shall, we shall be, we shall have, which you, which are, which will be, which will have, on, on the, on which, on this.

UNIT 7 *Drill 14*

We shall be judging some of the roses in the show which will be on the fourth in the old railway shed.
We have worked late to rush this page to you so that you may check it for the budget.
The girls say they will fetch your luggage but it will be a rush for them today.
I had a large share of the work, so I shall be in a rush to get it checked on Monday.
Which shades of yellow and red shall we have on the edges of the two rowing boats.
Say you will exchange the red coat and touch up the mauve shades for Kay on Wednesday.

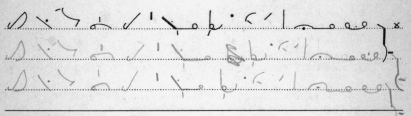

UNIT 9 *Drill 17*

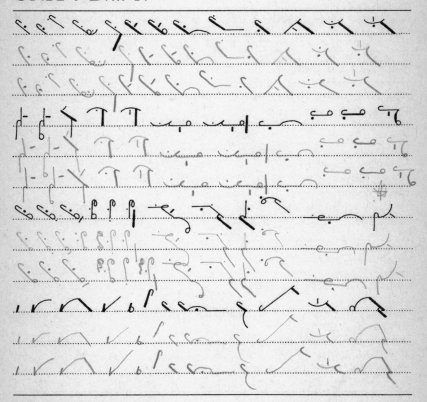

UNIT 9 *Drill 18*

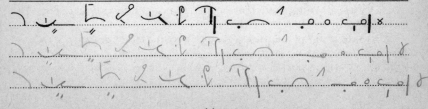

14

UNIT 4 *Drill 8*

We will be delayed and the sailing will be Monday, but we have had to stow the cases below decks.

We have sold the lengths of the yellow sails and we will have to make some.

This is the way to the lake and it will be safe to bathe today and sail the boat.

Yes, we have weighed the cake for Wednesday's wedding and have paid Kay for it.

We loaded the boat yesterday but you will have to delay the sailing to Wales for a month.

UNIT 5 *Drill 9*

ray, red, road, roads, roadway, rail, railway, railways, rose, roses, raising, rusk.

purpose, purposes, works, wear/ware, board, tear, girl, word, Thursday.

thorough, furrow, borough, air, errors, pairs, were, rare, care, resource, resources.

firms, term, yours, yourself, manufacture, manufacturer, manufactured, are, our, ours.

you are, we are, to our, of our, in your, they are, for us/his, of us/his, with us/his, and you, will you, with you, to his/us, with his/us.

UNIT 5 *Drill 10*

We are in your care and we know you will be fair to the girls and the customers.

Will you stay for some days to make repairs to the doors and restore the old desks?

All of our roses are red but the colour of your rare rose is pale yellow.

We manufacture for world airways and we do repairs for the railways.

Thank you for your welcome. This firm takes care of its customers.

UNIT 6 *Drill 11*

coat, coats, coating, cut, cuts, cutting, note, notes, court, fate, late, weight/wait, kept, left, wept.

bed, dead, results, resulting, resulted, expects, expecting, expected, method, methods, except.

ports, export, exports, support, supports, effect, select, locate, rate, rates.

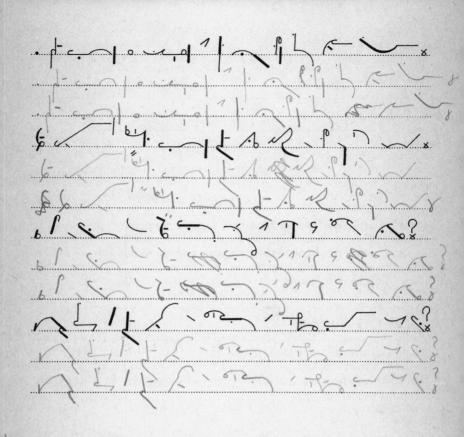

UNIT 10 *Drill 19*

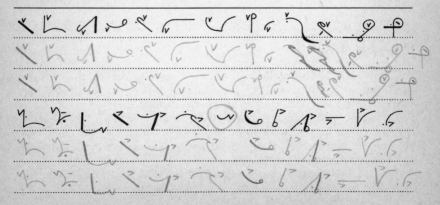

15

Anything you pay is going to his aid. I know you may do something to aid his case.

Do you make name tapes and may I pay today? Do you know his name?

UNIT 3 *Drill 5*

they, though, fade, fades, fading, foam, votes, voting, faith, both, bathes, bathing, facing, faces.

saves, saving, gets, getting, them, month, months, cup, cups, enough, meadow.

fame, famous, vague, vogue, supposing, supposes, doses, custom, desk, cases.

for, for the, have, having, have the, have they, to have, be, being, be the, this, this is, this is the, all, all the, with, with the.

thank, thanks, thanking, I thank, thank you, to thank you, of this, to this, in some, with them, to them, for them, I have, I have the, they have, they have the.

UNIT 3 *Drill 6*

Thank all the folk for voting this Sunday and Monday. They have faith in a vote for Ted.

They have come to stay in the bay, and this is the day for bathing and dozing in the sun.

The cases of oboes may have to go to the customs and it is up to you to pay for them.

The boat takes months and the deck is unsafe for the cases. Get Ted to stow them.

Does it make sense for them to get a bonus in May? No, they have enough.

UNIT 4 *Drill 7*

lay, leg, luck, lesson, yellow, load, scale, selling, delays, slow, vessel.
will, will be, I will, I will be, you will be, you will be the, it will be, it will be the, they will, they will be, you will have.
way, ways, sway, sways, well, swell, wake, wedding, we have, we have the, we know, we know the.
yesterday, young, yes, delay, delayed, weigh, weighed, weighed the, paid, paid the, thank, thanked, named.
as/has, as the/has the, and as/has, but, but you, but you will be the, but the, Monday, Wednesday, Sunday, May, is as, as is.

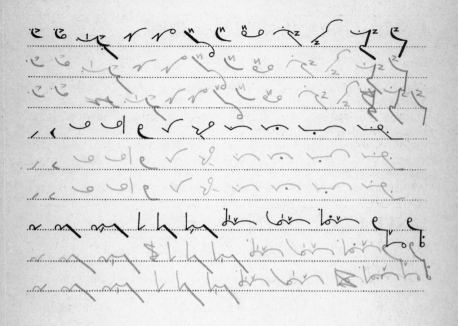

UNIT 10 *Drill 20*

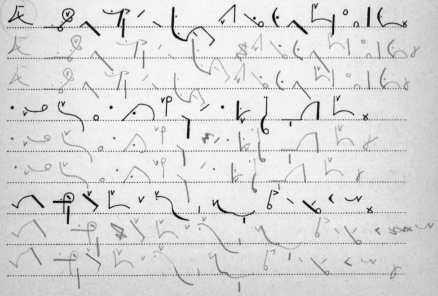

16

UNIT 1 *Drill 1*

pay, pays/pace, ape, apes, space, bay, bays/base, stay, stays, day, days/daze, aid, aids.

bait, baits, tape, tapes, date, dates, soap, soaps, pose, bow, oboe, obey, obeys.

toe/tow, toes/tows, oats, stow, stows, doe/dough, spades, boat, boats, toad, toads, dote, dotes.

the, it, is/his, it is, it is the, and, and is/his, is the, to, to his, today, of, of his.

pay the, tow the, to the, date the, of the, and the, aid the, to stay, is it, is to, *full stop, question mark, exclamation mark.*

UNIT 1 *Drill 2*

Date the tape today and space it. Today is the day to stow the tape and pay the aide.

Tape the boat today and tow it to the bay. It is his boat and the aide's tape.

It is his pay-day today. Pay the aide to stow the oats and tow the boat to the base.

The date of his pay-day is today. Stow the bait and pay, and tape the space.

His boat is to stay in the bay. Tape the spades and pay the aids today.

UNIT 2 *Drill 3*

ache, aim, know/no, go, bake, cape, take, tame, code, game.

cake, gate, case, snake, opaque, makes, combing, paying, boating.

own, owns, owning, smoke, smokes, smoking, aim the, to make, to make the.

I, I do, do, do you, it is, it is the, I know, I know the, in the, thing, anything, something, nothing.

I, and I, of the, of his, in his, to do, to stay, in any, in any case, in the case, you may, to go.

UNIT 2 *Drill 4*

I know the name of the boat in the bay and you do too. It is the same and you know it.

The aim today is to bake cakes and make cocoa to take to the boat.

Stow the case and take the two boats to the bay today. You may stay in the bay.

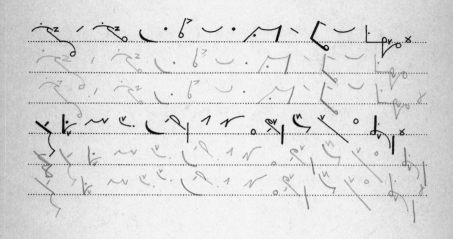

UNIT 11 *Drill 21*

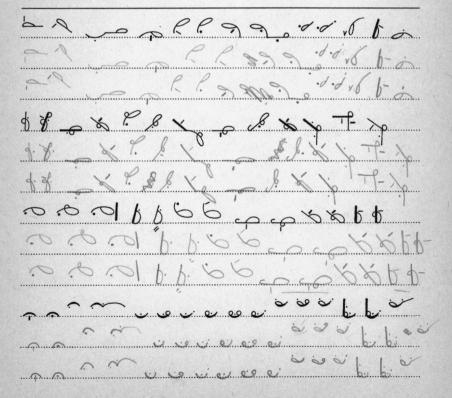

17

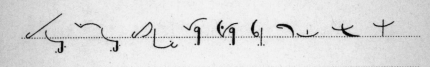

UNIT 25 *Drill 50*

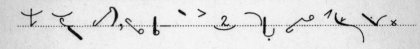

UNIT 11 *Drill 22*

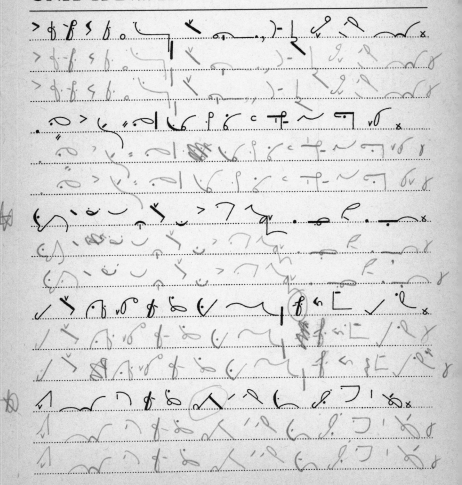

18

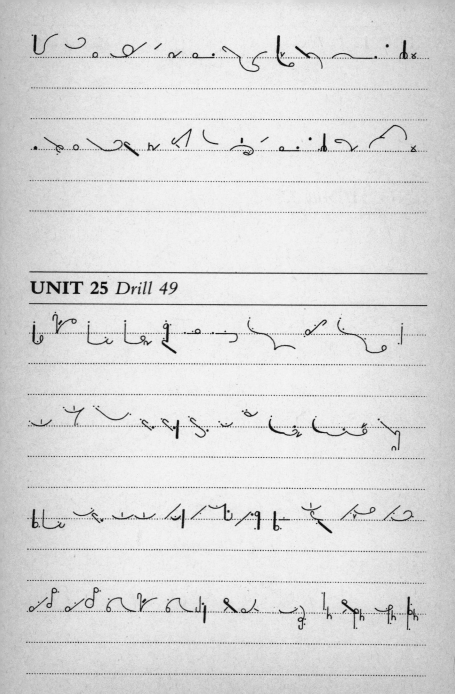

UNIT 25 *Drill 49*

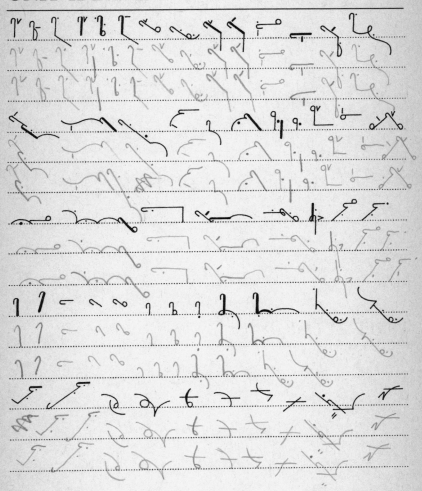

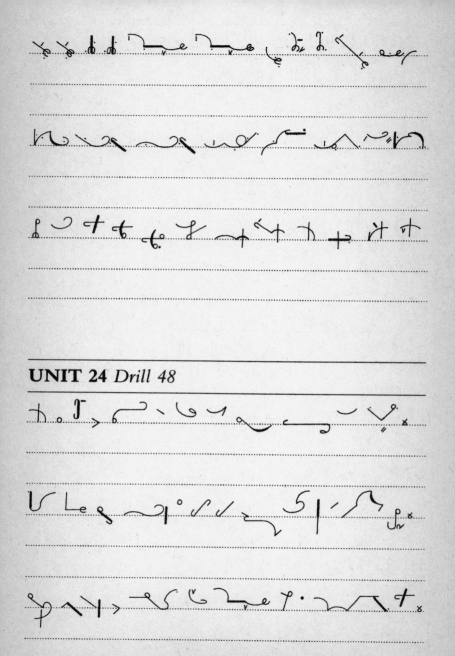

UNIT 24 *Drill 48*

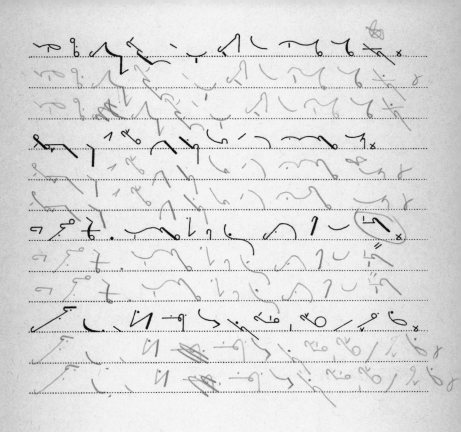

UNIT 13 Drill 25

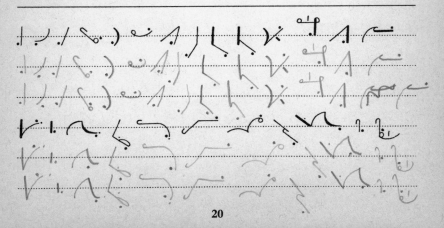

20

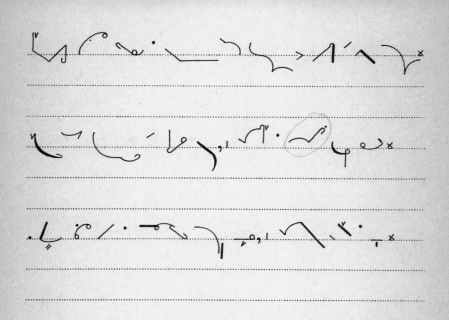

UNIT 24 *Drill 47*

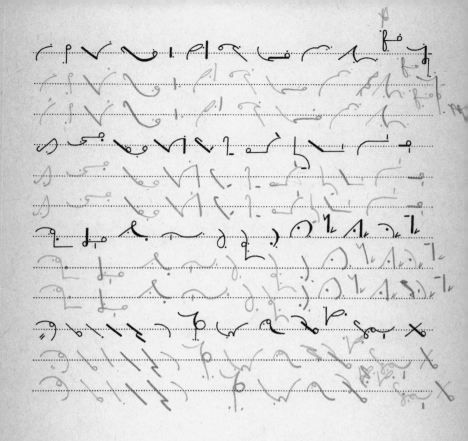

UNIT 13 *Drill 26*

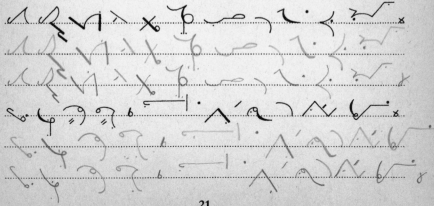

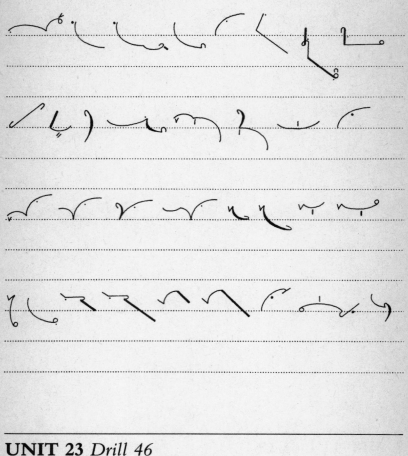

UNIT 23 *Drill 46*

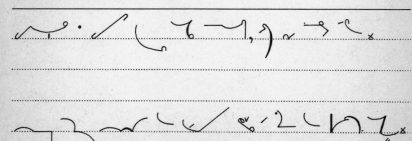

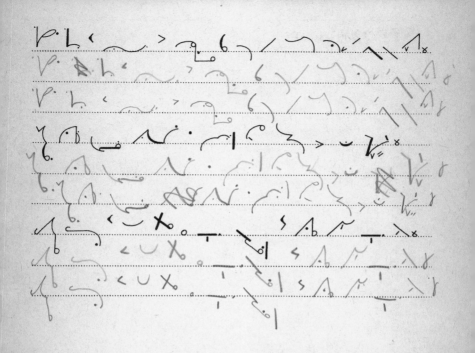

UNIT 14 *Drill 27*

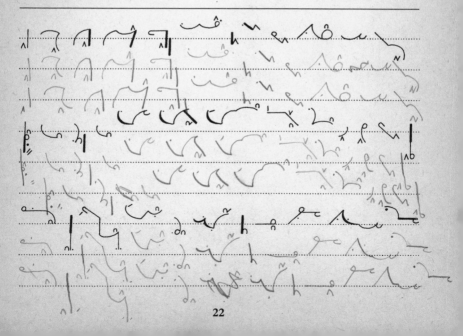

22

UNIT 23 *Drill 45*

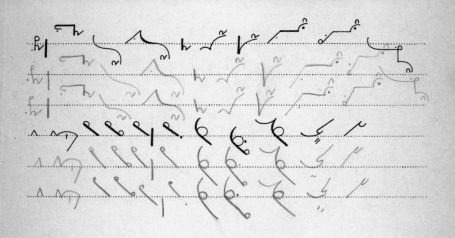

UNIT 14 *Drill 28*

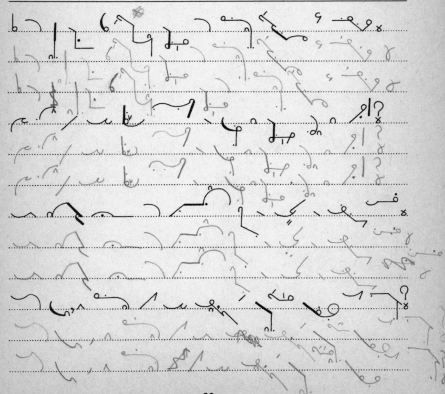

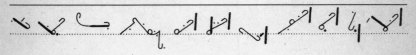

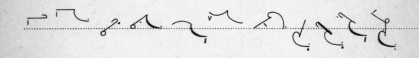

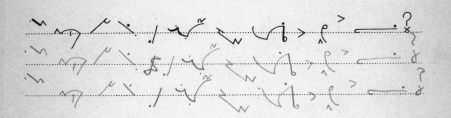

UNIT 15 *Drill 29*

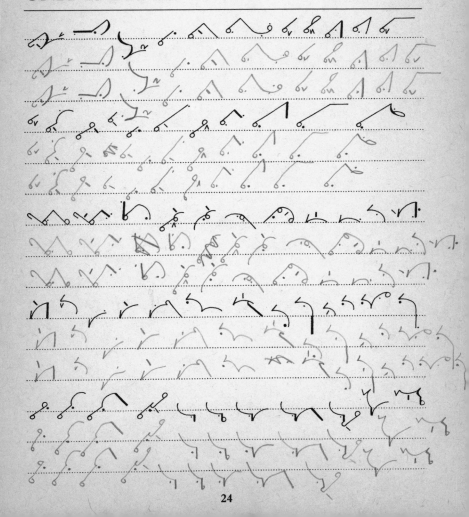

24

UNIT 21 *Drill 42*

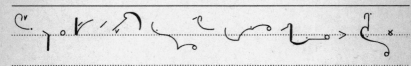

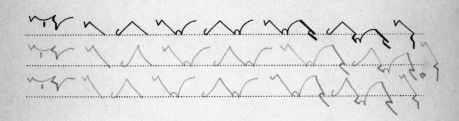

UNIT 15 *Drill 30*

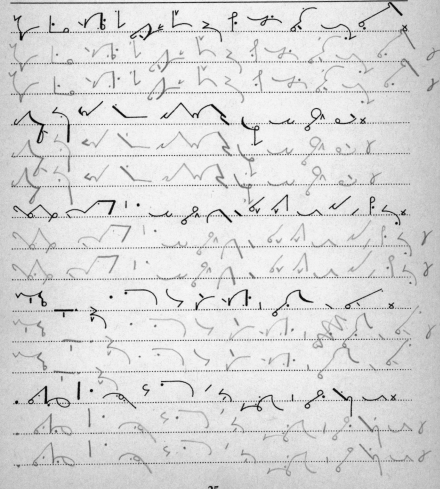

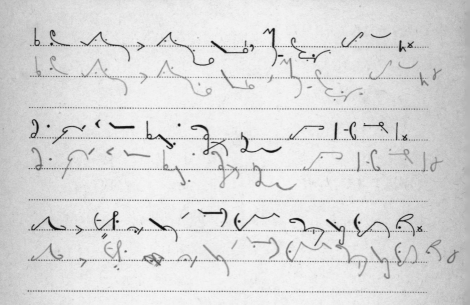

UNIT 21 *Drill 41*

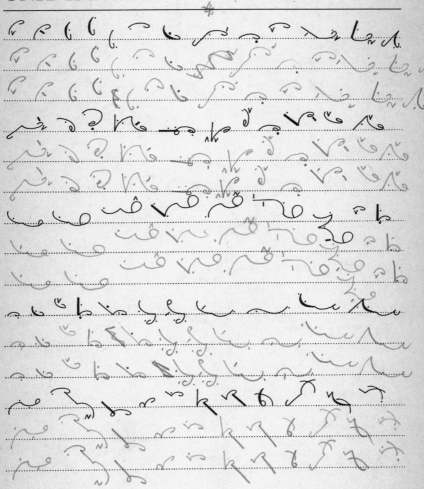

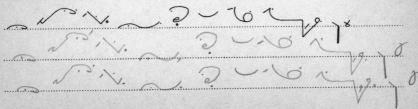

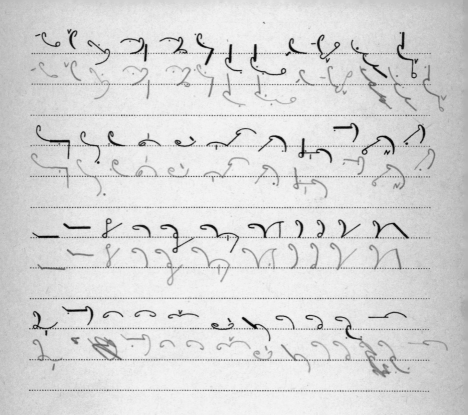

UNIT 20 *Drill 40*

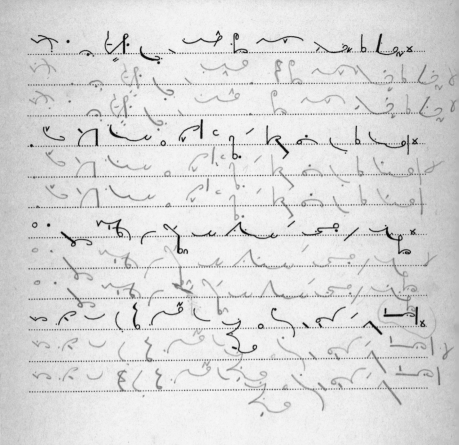

UNIT 17 *Drill 33*

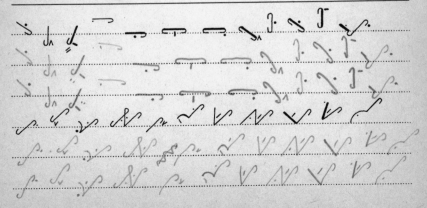

27

UNIT 19 *Drill 38*

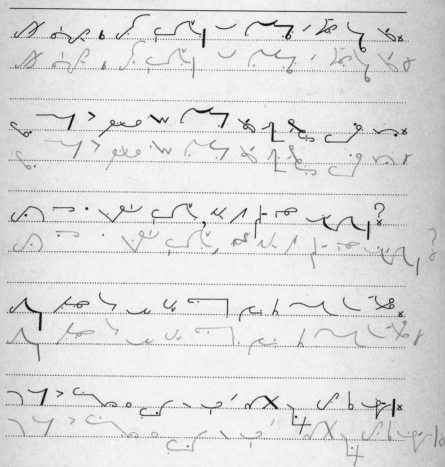

UNIT 20 *Drill 39*

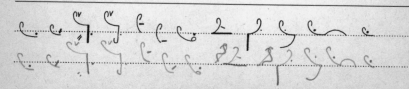

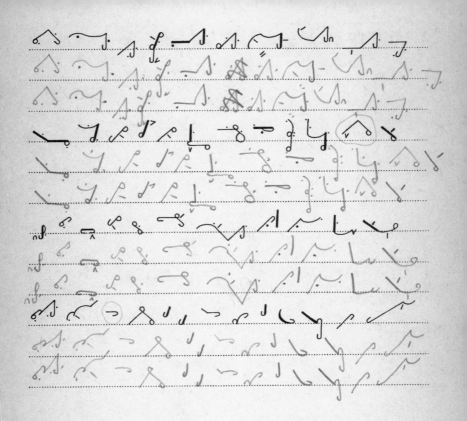

UNIT 17 *Drill 34*

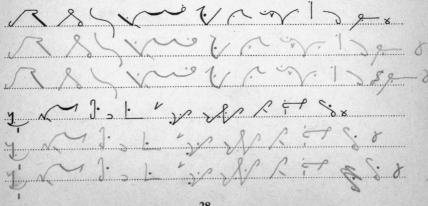

28

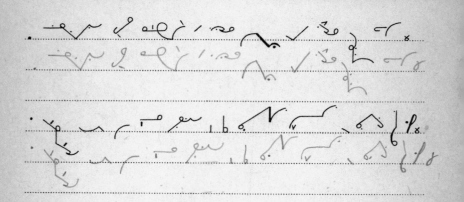

UNIT 19 *Drill 37*

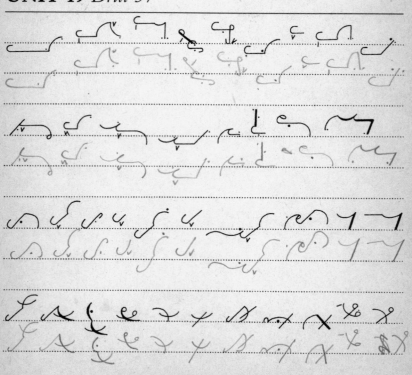

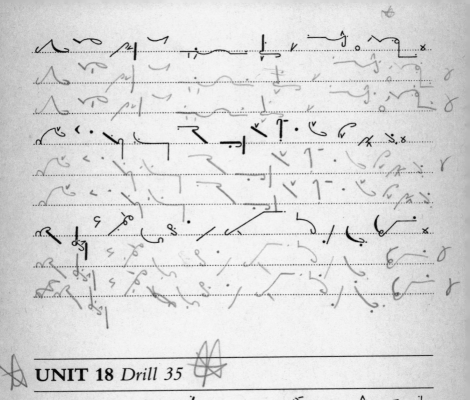

UNIT 18 *Drill 35*

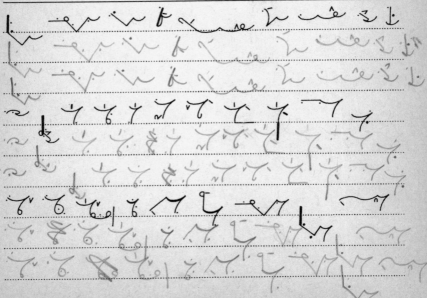

29

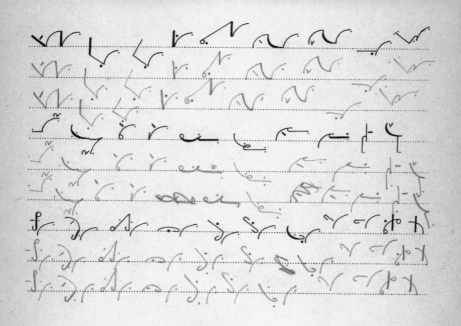

UNIT 18 *Drill 36*

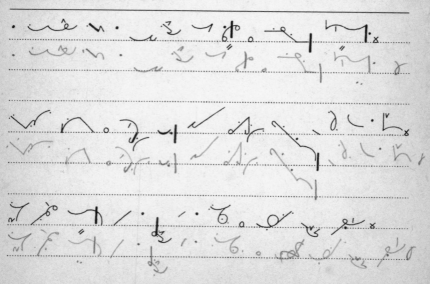

30